SECOND SERIES

More Classics to Moderns

Compiled and edited by Denes Agay

CONTENTS

Yorktown Music Press
London/New York/Sydney

Fughetta

Johann Sebastian Bach
(1685-1750)

Sonata

L.297

Domenico Scarlatti
(1685-1757)

Allegro Giocoso

Joseph Haydn
(1732–1809)

Da Capo senza replica

Minuet

K.335 (594a)

Wolfgang Amadeus Mozart
(1756-1791)

Bagatelle

Op.119, No.1

Ludwig van Beethoven
(1770-1827)

Scherzo
(Op. posth.)

Franz Schubert
(1797-1828)

14

Trio

legato

ped. simile

simile

pp

pp

Scherzo D. C.

Reverie
Träumerei (Op.15, No.7)

Robert Schumann
(1810–1856)

* Original

Youth Piece
Op.72, No.1

Felix Mendelssohn
(1809–1847)

Allegro moderato

Prelude
Op.28, No.20

Frédéric Chopin

*The E♭ according to the Polish Edition.

Waltz
Op.39, No.15

Johannes Brahms

Scherzo

from Op.27, Book 1, No.10

Dmitri Kabalevsky

Blindman's Buff

Op.15, No.3

Robert Schumann

Solitary Wanderer

Op.43, No.2

Edvard Grieg
(1843-1907)

Allegretto semplice

Two Moravian Dances

Leos Janacek
(1854–1928)

Prelude

Op.11, No.22

Alexander Scriabine
(1872-1915)

Serenade of the Doll

from *Children's Corner*

Claude Debussy
(1862–1918)

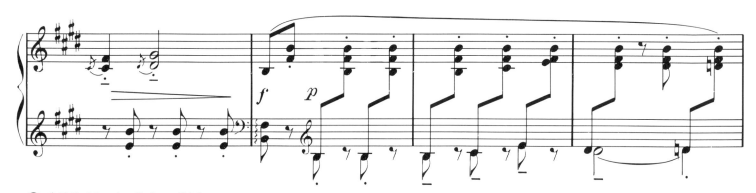

32

Exclusive distributors:
Music Sales Limited
8/9 Frith Street, London W1V 5TZ, England
Music Sales Pty. Limited,
120 Rothschild Avenue, Rosebery, NSW 2018, Australia.
Music Sales Corporation
257 Park Avenue South, New York, NY10010, U.S.A.

This book © Copyright 1979 by
Yorktown Music Press
ISBN 0.86001.681.1
Order No. YK 20162

Music Sales complete catalogue lists thousands of titles
and is free from your local music book shop, or direct from
Music Sales Limited. Please send a cheque/postal order
for £1.50 for postage to
Music Sales Limited, 8/9 Frith Street, London W1V 5TZ

Printed and bound in Great Britain by
Printwise (Haverhill) Limited, Haverhill, Suffolk